in the
11+ tests

11+
English
Success

Age 7–8

Age 8–9

Age 9–10

Age 10–11

10-Minute Tests

Sally Moon, Val Mitchell and Nick Barber

Sample page

clear instructional text

test and topic being covered

section number for quick reference

Test 3: Nouns and pronouns

Find the **proper nouns** in this passage and write them in the box below.

Last summer I went on holiday to Colorado in the United States. I stayed in a town called Estes Park, which is on the border of the Rocky Mountain National Park. After staying there for a week and attending a festival in a town called Lyons, I drove to Denver and caught a flight to Louisiana. My holiday was cut short because Hurricane Gustav meant that all tourists had to leave. Back home in England, I said to myself, 'Nick, you're a lucky man!'

21.	22.	23.	24.	25.
26.	27.	28.	29.	30.

Complete the following passage using *all* the **nouns** from the box below.

session	Ryan	entry	players	concern
imagination	they	amazement	coach	boys

All of the **(31)** _____ were excited. They had won a trip to a Premiership football

club. One of the boys, **(32)** _____, had entered a competition where he had to

use his **(33)** _____ to describe his dream day out. He had described going with

his friends to meet all their favourite football **(34)** _____ and take part in a training

(35) _____ with them. Fortunately, his **(36)** _____ was regarded as the

best one, and Ryan was filled with **(37)** _____ when he discovered that he could

take his schoolmates with him! Despite his **(38)** _____ that this was just a dream, the

day came and **(39)** _____ were taken to the club in an executive **(40)**

_____.

/40

9

total test score

2

Contents

Read the text below and then answer the questions that follow.

Pass it! Wizard

Scene 1

(Two boys are sitting on a wall behind a bus shelter with music blaring out from the speakers attached to an MP3 player. They are looking intently at the screen of a mobile phone.)

Hamid: Fancy meeting by the cinema again later?

Connor: Epic. I've told Dad I'm revising wi' you again tonight so we can really get it sorted. He'll be blown away when he sees our marks.

Hamid: Yea, this app's well smart. We'll have to sneak it past Mr Jones fust though, tha knows he checked everybody's pockets last year.

Connor: Nay problem for me. I've got a ripped lining in my jacket – I'm going put it on 'silent' and stuff it in theer.

(Connor's sister Jenna emerges through the ginnel and sees the boys engaged in what looks like a game on one of their phones.)

Connor: Quick, stop faffing about and switch ir off! You know what our Jenna's like, she's bound to blurt something out if she sees it.

(Hamid stuffs the phone hurriedly into his rucksack, nonchalantly swinging it over his shoulder.)

Jenna: I saw that Hamid. Connor, Dad's lookin' for you. He said it's important so you'd better move it.

Connor: Catch ya later mate.

(Connor winks at Hamid and slides down from the wall before sloping off into the house.)

Scene 2

(Connor walks into the kitchen where Dad's sitting with his laptop open, scouring intently through the contents of an email.)

Connor: What's up Dad?

Dad: You heard about this '*Pass it!* Wizard' app son?

(Connor shrugs innocently and tries to glance surreptitiously over his Dad's shoulder.)

Dad: (not waiting for a response) Apparently, according to Parent Mail, it's some crazy software that gives you the answers to exam questions. Schools are asking parents to confiscate their kids' phones during exam weeks.

            They used to call this country a democracy! You'd think they'd trust us to know our own kids. Flaming do-gooders.

Connor: Nowt I've ever heard of Dad. That it then?

(Connor begins sidling towards the door.)

Dad: Not so fast young man. Hand it over.

1. Where is the bus stop?
   a) next to the school   b) outside Hamid's house   c) near the cinema
   d) outside Connor's house   e) we are not told

2. What do the boys do as soon as Jenna arrives?
   a) show her the app   b) put the phone away   c) blurt something out
   d) go to see Dad   e) emerge through the ginnel

3. Why is Dad unlikely to see Connor again that evening?
   a) He is going to hide.   b) He is going to bed.   c) He is meeting Hamid.
   d) He is going to the cinema.   e) He is going out with Jenna.

4. Who are the 'Flaming do-gooders' likely to be?
   a) other children   b) other countries   c) parents
   d) software developers   e) school authorities

5. How are brackets used in this text?
   a) to separate 'asides'   b) to identify stage directions   c) to break up the text
   d) to highlight the introductions   e) as sub headings

6. Why are there two scenes in this text?
   a) they are separate stories   b) the characters have changed
   c) the setting has changed   d) the technology has changed   e) none of these

7. Where is this play likely to be set?
   a) the South of England   b) the North of England   c) the United States
   d) Australia   e) Ireland

8. What is a ginnel?
   a) a house   b) a toilet   c) a passage way   d) a phone   e) a bus stop

9. Which two words in the text show the boys are trying to keep the app a secret?
   1 intently   **2** secretly   **3** engaged   **4** hurriedly   **5** surreptitiously
   a) 1 and 4   b) 3 and 4   c) 1 and 2   d) 4 and 5   e) 2 and 5

10. When is the most likely time this text is set?
    a) Dickensian times   b) During the Second World War   c) 1960s
    d) 2012   e) 2000

/10

Test 2: Discussion texts

Read the text below and then answer the questions that follow.

Have children's lives changed for the good since the development of the Internet?

1 Since the development of the Internet we have been able to contact people living in different countries in a fraction of a second. Although this powerful innovation has brought with it tremendous advantages, it has also created its share of problems.

2 Developed in the 1960s so that universities and government research centres could exchange information, the Internet was not originally conceived for recreational use. Possibly because the technology was intended to create an environment of open discussion, the developers did not think too deeply about the dangers this would bring. Therefore, the fact that the Internet is now populated with a wide range of content unsuitable for children and offensive to many adults is hardly surprising.

3 Although Internet Service Providers and governments do not want to be seen to be censoring material, the consequence of this largely un-policed content is that the world has become a more dangerous place for children to live in. There are serious implications for both children's safety and their well-being as chat rooms and messaging services can be a forum for cyber-bullying and leave them vulnerable to contact with adults who may try to manipulate them.

4 However, the benefits of the technology have allowed children to keep in touch with their friends and relatives in a way that would have been impossible beforehand. Computers, tablets and mobile phones make it possible to chat for hours with people anywhere in the world and, with the increasing number of devices that support video, families can communicate across great distances, even if they cannot afford to travel to see each other.

5 The Internet also provides a wealth of knowledge and entertainment to educate and stimulate, allowing children to find out more about the lives of people in other countries and even make contact with them. Furthermore, as content expands, so does the sophistication of the screening tools to regulate it so making the Internet a safer place for children to spend time.

6 While the Internet has the capacity to harm young people and the challenge of providing a completely protected environment for children may never be completely met, the companionship, connections and cultural advantages it brings must indisputably transform their lives for the better.

1. For what use was the Internet originally envisaged?

   a) contacting people living in different countries   **b)** sharing information

   c) playing games   **d)** setting up video links   **e)** downloading music

2. Which words in the text give a negative impression of the Internet?

   1 contact   **2** un-policed   **3** sophistication   **4** protected   **5** bullying

   a) 1 and 4   **b)** 3 and 4   **c)** 1 and 2   **d)** 4 and 5   **e)** 2 and 5

3. From reading the text, how may the Internet negatively affect children's well-being?
   a) keeping in touch with their friends
   b) finding out new information
   c) reading other people's views about them
   d) learning about the lives of children in other countries
   e) interactive learning

4. Which innovation of the Internet, explained in the text, is saving people money?
   a) discount travel deals   b) online shopping   c) search facilities
   d) video phone calls   e) interactive games

5. Which two paragraphs deal with only the positive aspects of the Internet?
   a) 1 and 6   b) 3 and 4   c) 2 and 3   d) 4 and 5   e) 2 and 5

6. Which word in the text suggests that regulating the Internet will be difficult?
   a) innovation   b) challenge   c) protected   d) impossible   e) messaging

7. Which paragraph begins with a preposition?
   a) 1   b) 2   c) 3   d) 4   e) 5

8. Which of these statements most accurately reflects the writer's viewpoint?
   a) The Internet is dangerous and should be banned.
   b) The Internet is great for playing games.
   c) The Internet can improve children's lives.
   d) The Internet provides a protected environment for children.
   e) The tablet is the best device for keeping in touch with people.

9. Where might this article be published?
   a) tabloid headline article
   b) gossip magazine
   c) specialist technology magazine
   d) parent website
   e) Internet chat room

10. What does 'range' mean (paragraph 2)?
    a) review   b) game   c) set   d) graph   e) population

/10

Find the **common nouns** in this passage and write them in the correct column in the chart below.

Arthur sat down and was overcome with fear. The riverbank was wet and muddy but he found a log to sit on. He looked over the water and felt intense nervousness. The clouds in the sky seemed full of foreboding. Anger and sadness overwhelmed him.

Concrete	Abstract
1.	6.
2.	7.
3.	8.
4.	9.
5.	10.

Replace the underlined word with the correct **pronoun** in each of these sentences.

11. **Robert** married Tara.   _____

12. Robert married **Tara.**   _____

13. **My sister and I** went shopping.   _____

14. Alija brought **her present.**   _____

15. **Emma** has got a twin sister.   _____

16. **The goldfish** was swimming.   _____

17. **Laura** had long hair.   _____

18. Josh spoke to **the boys.**   _____

19. Suyash joined **the band.**   _____

20. **The band** hired Suyash as their singer.   _____

Find the **proper nouns** in this passage and write them in the box below.

Last summer I went on holiday to Colorado in the United States. I stayed in a town called Estes Park, which is on the border of the Rocky Mountain National Park. After staying there for a week and attending a festival in a town called Lyons, I drove to Denver and caught a flight to Louisiana. My holiday was cut short because Hurricane Gustav meant that all tourists had to leave. Back home in England, I said to myself, 'Nick, you're a lucky man!'

21.	22.	23.	24.	25.
26.	27.	28.	29.	30.

Complete the following passage using *all* the **nouns** from the box below.

session	Ryan	entry	players	concern
imagination	they	amazement	coach	boys

All of the **(31)** _____ were excited. They had won a trip to a Premiership football

club. One of the boys, **(32)** _____, had entered a competition where he had to

use his **(33)** _____ to describe his dream day out. He had described going with

his friends to meet all their favourite football **(34)** _____ and take part in a training

(35) _____ with them. Fortunately, his **(36)** _____ was regarded as the

best one, and Ryan was filled with **(37)** _____ when he discovered that he could

take his schoolmates with him! Despite his **(38)** _____ that this was just a dream, the

day came and **(39)** _____ were taken to the club in an executive **(40)**

_____.

/40

There are 10 **capital letters**, two **question marks**, an **exclamation mark** and two **full stops** missing from this passage. Underline the letters that should be in capitals and add the punctuation clearly.

1–15. everyone who dreams of being a superstar musician wants the money and the fame, but how many people want all the day-to-day hassles that go with such status imagine never being able to go to your local supermarket in your scruffy clothes and talk to jackie who works on the tills consider never being able to visit your relatives without making an appointment, because the paparazzi will be expecting you to turn up at your uncle Albert's house wouldn't that be awful you might say that having six-figure pay cheques would cancel all that out, but i wouldn't like it. ok, so you're number one in the charts and the BBC want you to do an interview – that's fine, but you can't even walk to the local shop to buy a new comb so that you look the part

Rewrite these sentences using **capital letters** in only the correct places.

16. The Rocky Mountain National Park Is In Colorado.

_____

17. Manchester Has Two Premiership Football Teams – City And United.

_____

18. Mr Cavendish Eats Biscuits Made In Scotland.

_____

19. Vitthal Went To Spain For His Easter Holiday.

_____

20. CD Players Will Be Obsolete In The Future.

_____

Write down an answer for each of the categories below.
There are lots of different answers you could use.

21. the name of a country in Europe   _____

22. the name of a planet   _____

23. the name of a famous musician or band   _____

24. the name of a company or organisation   _____

25. the name of a famous author   _____

Underline the letters that should be **capitals** in this passage.

26–35. gregory and jayne were flying on safeflight airlines to greece for their summer holiday

on a flight leaving heathrow at 09:30 bst and arriving in athens at 10:30 local time.

'i hope they'll be there to meet us,' he ventured nervously as they boarded their flight.

'i'm sure they'll make it,' she reassured him.

/35

Test 5: Plurals

> Write the **irregular plurals** for each of these nouns.

1. analysis _____
2. stimulus _____
3. axis _____
4. crisis _____
5. ox _____
6. oasis _____
7. woman _____
8. cod _____
9. deer _____
10. louse _____
11. child _____
12. kiss _____
13. fungus _____
14. species _____
15. goose _____
16. moose _____
17. offspring _____
18. emphasis _____
19. tooth _____
20. mouse _____

> Rewrite these nouns in their **plural** form.

21. butterfly _____
22. donkey _____
23. journey _____
24. cry _____
25. valley _____
26. company _____
27. play _____
28. turkey _____
29. quality _____
30. sky _____

Rewrite these nouns in their **plural** form.

31. elf _____

32. hope _____

33. advance _____

34. notice _____

35. church _____

36. match _____

37. battle _____

38. carbohydrate _____

39. knife _____

40. pickle _____

Change all of the underlined words into **plurals** in this passage so that it makes sense!

The **girl (41)** _____ went for a ride on their **pony (42)** _____

the morning after a terrible storm. Riding along, they noticed the

chimney (43) _____ on a nearby farm had been blown down.

The riders said to **themself (44)** _____ that they were lucky to live in

such well-built **house (45)** _____. As they rode off they noticed some

person (46) _____ selling **strawberry (47)** _____ by a river

who, it turned out, were **witness (48)** _____ to what had happened the

night before. As they all shared **story (49)** _____ about the event, the girls

didn't notice the **mosquito (50)** _____ and later discovered that they'd

all been bitten!

/50

> Read the text below and then answer the questions that follow.

The last bus

'See you tomorrow!' yelled Kirsty at the back of her friends' heads as they ambled off towards the Underground.

Strolling along towards the bus stop Kirsty smiled to herself. What a night! The film had been awesome. Even better, going to the late showing meant that the last bus would be along in five minutes so she wouldn't have long to wait in the December chill.

Glancing at her watch as she arrived at the shelter there was just time to get the change ready and she delved into her bag to find the purse. The keys rattled at the bottom as she pushed the contents left, then right, reaching for the familiar soft leather. Nothing. She could hear the bus coming around the corner so she dragged the contents out onto her knees to find it more easily. It wasn't there, nor was her mobile phone.

Butterflies filled her stomach as the bus drew up to the stop, excuses formulating and spinning around in her head as she threw her belongings back into the bag.

'Evening love,' the driver greeted her warmly as she clambered onto the platform in front of him. 'Everything alright?'

'I'm so sorry, I've lost my purse,' Kirsty began, '... and my phone's missing,' she blurted out, hearing the panic in her own voice and mentally telling herself off for being so pathetic.

'I think somebody's been through my bag in the foyer.'

The driver's demeanour changed quickly. A grey pallor spread across his previously healthy complexion and Kirsty felt her heart beating faster as she watched the transformation.

He sat back into the shadows of the cab, 'I know this is going to sound harsh, but I'm afraid you're going to have to get off.' The driver released the handbrake, revving up the engine.

'I can pay you tomorrow,' pleaded Kirsty. 'I can't get home any other way. Please, just this once. I'll write a really nice letter about you to the station manager.' The words tumbled out of her mouth like stones careering over a cliff top.

'I don't think that would work!' he replied gruffly and shuffled uneasily in his seat. 'I'm on report already for doing the same thing last month. Please, just step down miss.'

Sobbing, Kirsty turned and stumbled back into the dark street. She would have to start walking. Something Mum had told her never to do.

1. Where had Kirsty been?
   a) the Underground   **b)** the theatre   **c)** the youth club
   d) the cinema   **e)** her friend's house

2. What do we know is made of leather?
   a) Kirsty's bag   **b)** Kirsty's purse   **c)** the driver's jacket
   d) the bus seat   **e)** Kirsty's shoes

3. Which two signs indicate that the driver is likely to refuse to take Kirsty before he speaks?
   1 his manner altered   **2** his heart was beating faster   **3** butterflies filled his stomach
   4 he sat back   **5** he revved the engine

   a) 1 and 5   **b)** 2 and 4   **c)** 3 and 5   **d)** 4 and 5   **e)** 1 and 4

4. How many paragraphs begin with a verb?
   a) 1   **b)** 2   **c)** 4   **d)** 7   **e)** 9

5. What is the purpose of the ellipsis used when Kirsty speaks to the driver for the first time?
   a) something has been missed out   **b)** there is information to follow that is not included
   c) the dialogue is important   **d)** the passage of time   **e)** none of these

6. What language feature is the phrase, 'like stones careering over a cliff top'?
   a) simile   **b)** metaphor   **c)** alliteration   **d)** indefinite article   **e)** onomatopoeia

7. What could be the moral of this story?
   a) don't go out with your friends   **b)** don't wait for a late bus on your own
   c) always have the correct change   **d)** don't forget your purse
   e) get to bus stop early

8. Who has given Kirsty advice?
   a) her friends   **b)** the driver   **c)** the station manager
   d) her mother   **e)** the star of the film

9. How is the driver feeling?
   a) angry   **b)** uncomfortable   **c)** happy   **d)** rushed   **e)** tired

10. What is the meaning of 'pallor'?
    a) pale colour   **b)** mist   **c)** beard   **d)** poor   **e)** friend

/10

Read the text below and then answer the questions that follow.

The Northern Lights

Can you imagine a rainbow of colours swirling together in a dance across the sky? Then you should be able to imagine a phenomenon that occurs mainly at the North Pole called 'The Northern Lights'.

Also called the Aurora Borealis, these dancing lights occur at the northern magnetic pole and appear when solar winds combine with the Earth's atmosphere. An identical spectacle appears mainly at the South Pole and is called the Aurora Australis.

In 1621, Pierre Gassendi named this amazing natural display Aurora Borealis from the name of the Roman Goddess of dawn, Aurora, and the Greek name for the north wind, Boreas. In traditional Greenland mythology, the moving lights were thought to be spirits playing ball games with the skull of a walrus!

The Northern Lights appear when solar winds travel at speeds of about one million miles per hour towards the Earth. Guided by the Earth's magnetic field to the poles, the particles mix with the gases, oxygen and nitrogen, to produce differing colours of light. The colour depends on the height at which the particles and gases meet. As the particles and gases in the Aurora are continually moving, this creates the effect of dancing lights.

Aurora colour by altitude		
Gas	Altitude	Colour of light
oxygen	up to 150 miles	green
oxygen	above 150 miles	red
nitrogen	up to 60 miles	blue
nitrogen	above 60 miles	purple/violet

Whether you believe the scientific explanations or any of the various myths about the Aurora Borealis, one thing is for certain: it remains an enigmatic and spectacular natural wonder of the world.

1. In which two locations are dancing lights mainly found?

    1 Greece   2 Rome   3 The North Pole   4 The South Pole   5 Borealis

    a) 1 and 2   b) 2 and 5   c) 4 and 5   d) 3 and 4   e) 1 and 3

2. How fast do solar winds travel?

    a) above 150mph   b) under 60mph   c) about 1 000 000mph

    d) about 100 000mph   e) above 60mph

3. What causes the Northern Lights to change colour?
   a) the Earth's magnetic field
   b) the north wind
   c) the spirits playing ball games
   d) rainbows
   e) the movement of the particles and gases

4. Why did Pierre Gassendi use the word 'Borealis'?
   a) he saw them in Greece   b) they were in the south
   c) they move like the wind   d) they reminded him of walruses
   e) they occur at dawn

5. How are the Northern Lights different from a rainbow?
   a) the colours move around   b) they occur in the sky   c) they are colourful
   d) they are natural phenomena   e) they contain red and blue coloured light

6. What does the table tell you about the gases?
   a) how colour affects the height   b) how height affects the colour
   c) the attitude of different scientists   d) the density of the gases
   e) none of the above

7. What is the meaning of 'enigmatic' in the final paragraph?
   a) energetic   b) enduring   c) miniscule   d) engulf   e) mysterious

8. In which of these publications are you likely to find this text?
   a) Theatre Lighting Monthly   b) Geographic Monthly   c) Walrus World
   d) Greek and Roman Myths   e) Aurora's Anatomy

9. What type of text is 'The Northern Lights'?
   a) a traditional tale   b) a Greek saga   c) a Roman legend
   d) a Greenland myth   e) factual text

10. What kind of language feature is the phrase, 'wonder of the world'?
    a) personification   b) rhyme   c) onomatopoeia   d) alliteration   e) metaphor

/10

Circle the **verb** in bold which makes the most sense in these sentences.

Example: Stuart (strummed)/streamed/slammed his guitar rhythmically.

1. Paul **ran/ambled/walked** all the way to the shops as quickly as he could to get there before they closed.

2. Patek didn't **release/realise/counter** how much money he'd made.

3. The sauce **complimented/complemented/coordinated** the fish perfectly.

4. Jessica started to **quench/quiver/quaker** with fear.

5. The referee **impaired/umpired/unleashed** the game for the fans.

6. Bangi was so upset he did not **shout/communicate/generate** with his friends all night.

7. 'Don't **consort/console/consume** so many fizzy drinks!' reprimanded the teacher.

8. Lucie's **uninterested/disinterested/unadulterated** expression showed that she was bored.

9. Jake was **aloud/allowed/a loud** to go out when he'd finished his Maths homework.

10. Pretika had no time to **lose/loose/loan**, the bus would be arriving in five minutes!

Complete the following sentences using *all* the **verbs** from the box below.

brought   bought   cooked   ate   hurried

11. Chris _____ his drums and guitar to the concert.

12. King Alfred _____ the cakes until they were burnt.

13. Nicky _____ sausage and mash last Friday.

14. Irene _____ six pencils and a pencil case for five pounds.

15. Ellie _____ away because she didn't want her photograph taken.

Underline the correct form of the **verbs** in bold in these sentences.

Example: Dangerous tigers **was/were** running loose.

16. Donna **was/were** having a party.

17. Donna and Tracy **was/were** organising the reception.

18. Brenton **is/are** coming to the match.

19. Sean and David **is/are** going to the cinema.

20. Mike and Neil **are/is** neighbours.

21. Scientists **is/are** working on a cure for the common cold.

22. Noise **was/were** a problem for people living next to the main road.

23. The results **is/are** final.

24. Why did the others ask if they **was/were** coming along?

25. Marie **is/are** getting ready for the meal.

Complete these sentences with the correct form of the **verb** by using: *is*, *are*, *was* or *were*.

Example: Marie **was** working last week but not next week.

26. _____ James going to see Michelle next week?

27. Michelle and Emma _____ staying at their mum's house when the power cut happened.

28. Andrew _____ taking pictures of the surfers when he dropped his camera.

29. Courtney _____ finishing her essay when the teacher asked them to stop.

30. 'Look over there! Rocky _____ playing with the kittens.'

31. Kurt _____ living in Kentucky now.

32. Nobody knew if Dorothy _____ telling the truth about her lottery win.

33. Johanna _____ baking gingerbread biscuits; they smell lovely!

34. Marie-José _____ looking for her keys yesterday.

35. Richard _____ getting ready to perform at this very minute.

/35

These sentences should be split into two so that they make sense. Add in the missing **full stops** and underline any letters that should be changed to **capitals**.

1. The captain spoke to the crew he told them that all was well.

2. Vijya got in touch with a long-lost friend she hadn't seen her for years.

3. Puppies are cute they do make a mess though.

4. The band came from Melbourne in Australia in Australia, Melbourne is famous for great bands.

5. Dwayne ran he didn't want to miss the bus.

6. Molly visited her friend she didn't want to, really.

7. The new girl settled into the school she already knew some of the people there.

8. The library had thousands of books they didn't have the one that Luke wanted, however.

9. The volcano erupted lava shot out into the sky.

10. Leah put on her make-up it didn't make her feel better.

Rewrite these sentences by removing the **connectives** and turning them into two separate sentences.

11. Kadir played the sitar professionally at the concert, but no one liked it.

_____

_____

12. Hannah bought six pairs of jeans but wore each pair only once!

_____

_____

13. The team lost because they played badly on the day of the match.

_____

_____

14. The oil painting was no longer valuable since it had been damaged.

_____

_____

15. Singing wasn't Reece's favourite activity, because he got embarrassed.

_____

_____

Joe's computer keyboard is faulty. All the full stops have come out as commas and the capitals don't work. Highlight the seven **commas** that should be **full stops** and underline any letters that should be changed to **capitals**.

16–30. i went fishing down the canal with the gang, there were actually fish in the water, not just old trolleys, the sort you get at supermarkets, random metal work and litter, sam pulled one out first, a small roach with red fins, we were all amazed that something so beautiful could live in such a grotty place, andy landed a pike using a spoon lure, you should have seen his face when it bit his finger, everyone fell about laughing, even smiler,

/30

All of these **verbs** end in *y*. Change them to the past tense.

1. reply _____

2. fortify _____

3. clarify _____

4. spy _____

5. fry _____

6. pay _____

7. enjoy _____

8. portray _____

9. buy _____

10. volley _____

11. rely _____

12. carry _____

13. cry _____

14. say _____

15. sway _____

The words in the chart have been changed from words that originally ended in *y*. Write the *original words* in the spaces provided. The first one has been done for you.

Word	Original ending in *y*
tried	try
16. stupefied	
17. rectified	
18. babies	
19. beautiful	
20. dryer	
21. heaviness	
22. earliest	
23. trays	
24. mollifies	
25. shied	

Add the bold **word endings** to each word, correcting the spelling if necessary.

26. **ing** bake _____

27. **ly** formal _____

28. **ed** deter _____

29. **ed** pant _____

30. **est** quick _____

31. **ing** swim _____

32. **ed** benefit _____

33. **ly** magical _____

34. **er** happy _____

35. **er** sad _____

36. **ly** careful _____

37. **ing** shape _____

Choose the option in which all three words are spelt correctly to complete each sentence.

38. The light bulb was ... by Thomas Edison in 1879 ... a way to ... illuminate people's homes.

   a) invented/provideing/safely

   b) invented/providing/safely

   c) invented/providing/safley

   d) inventted/providding/safely

39. The ... were superb! Diamonds, sapphires and ... in bracelets, ... and necklaces.

   a) jewells/rubies/earrings

   b) jewels/rubys/earrings

   c) jewels/rubys/earings

   d) jewels/rubies/earrings

40. The ... howled and the ... huddled around the lower ... of the fir trees.

   a) wolves/deer/branches

   b) wolfs/deer/branches

   c) wolves/deers/branchies

   d) wolfs/deer/branchs

/40

Read the text below and then answer the questions that follow.

The apis dawn

1   Like the spores from a primeval fungus, they rose
    somnolently through the morning mist. So deep
    was the distant drone that it barely reached the
    consciousness of the conservation worker opening the
    visitor centre on the marshes, and he idly swiped the air
    above his head as the mass moved off behind him.

2   Looking down from his Deptford flat, Vitthal heard waves
    slapping violently against the gnarled wooden pier below.
    As usual, Mum had left for the hospital at 4am and he
    was alone. Feeling bored, he breathed indolently onto the
    window so that he could write his name.

3   The noise was imperceptible at first – a distant rumbling
    like the deep-throated growling of a cougar about to
    pounce and as he traced the letters on the cold pane, he could feel a faint vibration running
    through his fingers. Curious about the origin of the sound, Vitthal turned to look past the O_2
    Arena, the direction the noise seemed to be emanating from. Squinting hard to get a better
    view, he could just make out a bank of dark mist building up where the river meandered out of
    sight. But as the boy fixed his gaze, he realised it wasn't a mist at all but skeins of gigantic bees
    swarming up the river. Surely they couldn't be real?

4   At RAF Swanton Flight Lieutenant Andrews had picked up what appeared to be a squadron
    of aircraft travelling on an unauthorised flight path across South London. He called the officer
    in charge. Unable to raise the aircraft, the station siren sounded and they went to red alert,
    scrambling a reconnaissance flight to investigate. Somehow Andrews knew that this wasn't just
    another unscheduled exercise.

5   Now Vitthal could see them clearly. Rotating their monstrous heads menacingly from left to
    right, their piercing blue eyes bulged above huge razor-sharp mandibles as the cloud of insects
    scanned the terrain below. Inch by inch the small boy lowered himself down below the window
    ledge and cowered out of sight.

6   Then as if from out of nowhere, the thunderous blades of a helicopter rose from behind the Dockland
    apartments and swung down into the path of the advancing swarm. The pilot swiftly trained his sights
    on the centre of the apis horde surging aggressively towards him and prepared to fire.

7   A white heat surged through the cockpit as the instrument panels went blank and high on the
    16th floor of an apartment overlooking the river, a young spectator cried out in the silence. The
    helicopter shimmered and disappeared without a sound.

1. Which sound did Vitthal not hear?
   a) slapping waves   b) thunderous blades   c) deep-throated growling
   d) his own cry   e) a siren

2. Which one of these collective nouns is not used for the bees?
   a) flight   b) swarm   c) horde   d) cloud   e) mass

3. Which two adverbs indicate to the reader that the bees are hostile?
   1 violently   2 menacingly   3 indolently   4 imperceptibly   5 aggressively
   a) 1 and 2   b) 1 and 5   c) 2 and 5   d) 3 and 4   e) 4 and 5

4. What does the word 'apis' mean in paragraph 6?
   a) bees   b) apes   c) gun sights   d) wings   e) hives

5. Why did the boy lower himself below the window ledge?
   a) he was tired   b) to get a better view
   c) Mum had told him to   d) his knees gave way
   e) he didn't want to be seen

6. What language feature does the writer repeat in paragraph 1?
   a) onomatopoeia   b) assonance   c) simple sentences
   d) personification   e) alliteration

7. What device does the writer use in paragraph 3 to involve the reader?
   a) a metaphor   b) a question   c) personification
   d) assonance   e) simple sentences

8. Which paragraphs are not set in Deptford?
   a) 1   b) 4   c) 1 and 4   d) 1 and 2   e) 4 and 6

9. What decade is this story set in?
   a) 1940s   b) 1950s   c) 1960s   d) 1980s   e) 2010s

10. What does 'unable to raise the aircraft' mean?
    a) the aircraft were lost   b) the aircraft couldn't take off
    c) the aircraft were too heavy   d) they couldn't be contacted
    e) the aircraft were buried

/10

Read the text below and then answer the questions that follow.

The Bully Bandit

Congratulations on your purchase of this unique device designed to defuse tricky situations in the playground.

Contents
Before assembling your Bully Bandit, check you have all the items
listed below:

- Instruction manual
- 4 x AAA batteries
- Remote control pad
- Safety wristband
- Reflective vest

! IMPORTANT: Read all instructions before use. Incorrect usage may result in personal injury.

The manufacturer cannot be held responsible for products that have not been registered for the extended five-year warranty programme within three weeks of purchase.

Setting up your device
Follow these instructions to set up your device safely:

1. Put on the reflective vest.
2. Secure the safety wristband using one of the loops at the base of the device. With the screen pointing towards you, attach the band to the loop on the left for left-hand operation or the loop on the right for right-hand operation.
3. Insert the batteries. You will hear a double bleep when they are inserted correctly. Reinsert the batteries if there is no audible sound.
4. Flick the red button on the base of the device to activate the touch screen.
5. Work through the guidance in the software launch application to input your personal data. When the device is ready you will feel a small electric shock on your index finger. Do not be alarmed, this is nothing to worry about.
6. Use the inbuilt camera to photograph potential bullies and save them into the archive. This will allow you to keep track of the number of 'hits'.
7. Test the device on a small animal, such as a frog or hamster, before using the Bully Bandit for the first time. This is completely safe.
8. Point the device at the 'target' animal and press 'Bully Freeze' on the screen while pointing the arrow icon at the head or chest.
9. When the animal (or bully) has been correctly targeted they will shiver slightly, then appear to freeze. A bluish colour is absolutely normal.
10. This temporary frozen state of your target will allow you to retrieve any stolen property without fear of confrontation and walk away from the situation in safety.
   Please note: the effect of the Bully Bandit will wear off after two minutes by which time you should ensure that you are safely out of sight and have alerted a responsible adult.

1. What is it essential to do in the first three weeks after purchase?
   - **a)** set up your device
   - **b)** read the safety instructions
   - **c)** register for the five-year warranty
   - **d)** buy four AAA batteries
   - **e)** alert a responsible adult

2. How will you know that the device has been aimed accurately?
   - **a)** the target will stop moving
   - **b)** you will feel a small electric shock
   - **c)** you will hear a double bleep
   - **d)** a red light will come on
   - **e)** the target will fall over

3. How do you know that this is the only product of its kind on the market?
   - **a)** it has an inbuilt camera
   - **b)** it has a Bully Freeze icon
   - **c)** it is a unique device
   - **d)** it is new
   - **e)** it has a launch application

4. Why might this device not always be effective?
   - **a)** it has a five-year warranty
   - **b)** you could only use it in the playground
   - **c)** everybody would have one
   - **d)** it gives you an electric shock
   - **e)** your clothing would give you away

5. Which two devices are not used to organise the text?
   1 bullets   **2** numbers   **3** text box   **4** glossary   **5** caption
   - **a)** 1 and 5
   - **b)** 4 and 5
   - **c)** 2 and 4
   - **d)** 3 and 4
   - **e)** 2 and 5

6. Which part of speech is used to reassure the reader in point 9?
   - **a)** adjective
   - **b)** pronoun
   - **c)** indefinite article
   - **d)** adverb
   - **e)** verb

7. Which instruction points do not begin with an imperative verb?
   - **a)** 5 and 8
   - **b)** 2 and 9
   - **c)** 9 and 10
   - **d)** 3 and 10
   - **e)** 5 and 6

8. Which statement about the Bully Bandit is true?
   - **a)** an alarm sounds when a bully is near
   - **b)** it has a memory function
   - **c)** it requires 4 AA batteries
   - **d)** the frozen state wears off after three minutes
   - **e)** the device must be tested on a frog

9. When would your Bully Bandit make a sound?
   - **a)** when the batteries are inserted correctly
   - **b)** when it is targeted correctly
   - **c)** when you switch it on
   - **d)** when you touch the screen
   - **e)** when you get an electric shock

10. How do you know that this product could be dangerous?
   - **a)** it has a five-year warranty
   - **b)** it has a safety wristband
   - **c)** it has a reflective vest
   - **d)** the instructions provide a warning
   - **e)** it says don't worry!

/10

Circle the **adjectives** in these sentences.

1. The dull, dreary day carried on as it had started.

2. Happy people work hard.

3. Exciting football matches happen frequently.

4. The cute hamsters ate their food.

5. Jordan walked past the tall, imposing gate.

6. Lauren's jewellery was expensive.

7. Loud shouts were heard from the playground.

8. The skilful forward raced past the weak defender.

9. There were no more fashionable shoes left in the sale.

10. Aaron sang his humorous songs.

Tick the correct column on the chart to indicate whether the word ending in *ly* is an **adverb** or an **adjective**.

Sentence	Adverb	Adjective
11. The **holy** man spoke well.		
12. Harrison ate the food **nervously**.		
13. **Ugly** creatures are scary.		
14. **Smelly** streets need cleaning.		
15. **Carefully**, Grace packed her bags.		
16. Caesar **triumphantly** entered Rome.		
17. The teacher's **kindly** ways made him popular.		
18. Emma disliked walking in the **chilly** weather.		
19. His **surly** looks scared people off.		
20. Ellie walked rather **anxiously** into the exam room.		

Complete the following passage using *all* the **adjectives** from the box below.

dilapidated   deserted   creaking   furtive   overgrown

The **(21)** _____ man walked through the **(22)** _____ village. He

entered the **(23)** _____ garden and approached the **(24)** _____

door. The house looked **(25)** _____.

Now use different **adjectives** to change the mood of the story so that the atmosphere is cheerful.

The **(26)** _____ man walked through the **(27)** _____ village. He

entered the **(28)** _____ garden and approached the **(29)** _____

door. The house looked **(30)** _____.

Complete the following passage using *all* the **adverbs** from the box below.

automatically   briskly   clearly   curtly   surreptitiously

The teacher walked **(31)** _____ into the class. After **(32)** _____

calling the register, she wrote the learning objective **(33)** _____ on the

whiteboard. Glancing **(34)** _____ around the classroom she saw the boy playing

(35) _____ with his phone.

/35

Test 14: Commas, question marks and exclamation marks

> Put the **commas** into these sentences.

1. Emma bought beans peppers and potatoes for dinner.
2. Despite being very clever Chloe got low marks on the test.
3. Jack Adam and their sisters emptied the car for Mum.
4. All people have talents but some have more useful talents than others.
5. Etsuku was a great runner despite getting blisters easily.
6. Unfortunately Jake didn't revise properly.
7. Nadia bought shoes shoes and more shoes in the sale.
8. Sakima despite his youth did extremely well in the competition.
9. Amy although she came last enjoyed the marathon run.
10. Whenever she pressed the bell she got a slight electric shock.

> Tick the columns in the chart to indicate whether
> the **commas** are correctly placed in each sentence.

Sentence	Correctly placed	Incorrectly placed
11. Mikio ate the biscuits, but left the bread.		
12. Laura, ate the bread but left the biscuits.		
13. Tenisa, despite being inexperienced, won the match for the girls.		
14. Cara didn't like her present, despite it being expensive.		
15. Josh, played the bass.		
16. Giorgio ate cabbage sprouts, and mushrooms.		
17. Isaac's shoes were black, red and gold.		
18. Liam and Tom formed a band, although they couldn't play any instruments.		
19. Kellie, shocked at what she read, gave Mark a telling-off.		
20. Rob, smiled lazily.		

English 10-Minute Tests Answers

Test 1

1.	d	2.	b
3.	c	4.	e
5.	b	6.	c
7.	b	8.	c
9.	d	10.	d

Test 2

1.	b	2.	e
3.	c	4.	d
5.	d	6.	b
7.	a	8.	c
9.	d	10.	c

Test 3

1–10. Concrete common nouns: riverbank, log, water, clouds, sky
Abstract common nouns: fear, nervousness, foreboding, anger, sadness

11.	He	12.	her
13.	We	14.	it
15.	She	16.	It
17.	She	18.	them
19.	them	20.	They

21. Colorado
22. United States
23. Estes Park
24. Rocky Mountain National Park
25. Lyons
26. Denver
27. Louisiana
28. Hurricane Gustav
29. England
30. Nick

31.	boys	32.	Ryan
33.	imagination	34.	players
35.	session	36.	entry
37.	amazement	38.	concern
39.	they	40.	coach

Test 4

1–15. Everyone who dreams of being a superstar musician wants the money and the fame, but how many people want all the day-to-day hassles that go with such status? Imagine never being able to go to your local supermarket in your scruffy clothes and talk to Jackie who works on the tills. Consider never being able to visit your relatives without making an appointment, because the paparazzi will be expecting you to turn up at your Uncle Albert's house. Wouldn't that be awful? You might say that having six-figure pay cheques might cancel all that out, but I wouldn't like it. OK, so you're number one in the charts and the BBC want you to do an interview – that's fine, but you can't even walk to the local shop to buy a new comb to make sure that you look the part!

16. The Rocky Mountain National Park is in Colorado.
17. Manchester has two Premiership football teams – City and United.
18. Mr Cavendish eats biscuits made in Scotland.
19. Vitthal went to Spain for his Easter holiday.
20. CD players will be obsolete in the future.
21–25. Many answers are possible although all must be proper nouns and begin with capital letters, e.g. Switzerland, Mars, Coldplay, Letts, Philip Pullman.
26–35. Gregory and Jayne were flying on Safeflight Airlines to Greece for their summer holiday on a flight leaving Heathrow at 09:30 BST and arriving in Athens at 10:30 local time. 'I hope they'll be there to meet us,' he ventured nervously as they boarded their flight. 'I'm sure they'll make it,' she reassured him.

Test 5

1.	analyses	2.	stimuli
3.	axes	4.	crises
5.	oxen	6.	oases
7.	women	8.	cod
9.	deer	10.	lice
11.	children	12.	kisses
13.	fungi	14.	species
15.	geese	16.	moose
17.	offspring	18.	emphases
19.	teeth	20.	mice
21.	butterflies	22.	donkeys
23.	journeys	24.	cries
25.	valleys	26.	companies
27.	plays	28.	turkeys
29.	qualities	30.	skies
31.	elves	32.	hopes
33.	advances	34.	notices
35.	churches	36.	matches
37.	battles	38.	carbohydrates
39.	knives	40.	pickles
41.	girls	42.	ponies
43.	chimneys	44.	themselves
45.	houses	46.	people
47.	strawberries	48.	witnesses
49.	stories	50.	mosquitoes

Test 6

1.	d	2.	b
3.	e	4.	c (see, strolling, glancing, sobbing)
5.	d	6.	a
7.	b	8.	d
9.	b	10.	a

Test 7

1.	d	2.	c
3.	e	4.	c
5.	a	6.	b
7.	e	8.	b
9.	e	10.	d

Test 8

1.	ran	2.	realise
3.	complemented	4.	quiver
5.	umpired	6.	communicate
7.	consume	8.	uninterested
9.	allowed	10.	lose
11.	brought	12.	cooked
13.	ate	14.	bought
15.	hurried		
16.	was	17.	were
18.	is	19.	are
20.	are	21.	are
22.	was	23.	are
24.	were	25.	is
26.	Is	27.	were
28.	was	29.	was
30.	is	31.	is
32.	was	33.	is
34.	was	35.	is

Test 9

1. The captain spoke to the crew. He told them that all was well.
2. Vijya got in touch with a long-lost friend. She hadn't seen her for years.
3. Puppies are cute. They do make a mess though.
4. The band came from Melbourne in Australia. In Australia, Melbourne is famous for great bands.
5. Dwayne ran. He didn't want to miss the bus.
6. Molly visited her friend. She didn't want to, really.
7. The new girl settled into the school. She already knew some of the people there.
8. The library had thousands of books. They didn't have the one that Luke wanted, however.
9. The volcano erupted. Lava shot out into the sky.
10. Leah put on her make-up. It didn't make her feel better.
11. Kadir played the sitar professionally at the concert. No one liked it.
12. Hannah bought six pairs of jeans. She wore each pair only once!

13. The team lost. They played badly on the day of the match.
14. The oil painting was no longer valuable. It had been damaged.
15. Singing wasn't Reece's favourite activity. He got embarrassed.
16–30. I went fishing down the canal with the gang. There were actually fish in the water, not just old trolleys, the sort you get at supermarkets, random metal work and litter. Sam pulled one out first, a small roach with red fins. We were all amazed that something so beautiful could live in such a grotty place. Andy landed a pike using a spoon lure. You should have seen his face when it bit his finger. Everyone fell about laughing, even Smiler.

Test 10
1. replied
2. fortified
3. clarified
4. spied
5. fried
6. paid
7. enjoyed
8. portrayed
9. bought
10. volleyed
11. relied
12. carried
13. cried
14. said
15. swayed
16. stupefy
17. rectify
18. baby
19. beauty, beautify
20. dry
21. heavy
22. early
23. tray
24. mollify
25. shy
26. baking
27. formally
28. deterred
29. panted
30. quickest
31. swimming
32. benefited
33. magically
34. happier
35. sadder
36. carefully
37. shaping
38. b
39. d
40. a

Test 11
1. e
2. a
3. c
4. a
5. e
6. e
7. b
8. c
9. e
10. d

Test 12
1. c
2. a
3. c
4. e
5. b
6. d
7. c
8. b
9. a
10. d

Test 13
1. dull, dreary
2. Happy
3. Exciting
4. cute
5. tall, imposing
6. expensive
7. Loud
8. skilful, weak
9. fashionable
10. humorous
11–20. Adverbs: 12, 15, 16, 20
Adjectives: 11, 13, 14, 17, 18, 19
21. furtive
22. deserted
23. overgrown
24. creaking
25. dilapidated
26–30. Many answers are possible, but the adjectives used should create a cheerful atmosphere.
31. briskly
32. curtly
33. clearly
34. automatically
35. surreptitiously

Test 14
1. Emma bought beans, peppers and potatoes for dinner.
2. Despite being very clever, Chloe got low marks on the test.
3. Jack, Adam and their sisters emptied the car for Mum.
4. All people have talents, but some have more useful talents than others.
5. Etsuku was a great runner, despite getting blisters easily.
6. Unfortunately, Jake didn't revise properly.
7. Nadia bought shoes, shoes and more shoes in the sale.
8. Sakima, despite his youth, did extremely well in the competition.
9. Amy, although she came last, enjoyed the marathon run.

10. Whenever she pressed the bell, she got a slight electric shock.
11–20. Correctly used commas: 11, 13, 14, 17, 18, 19
Incorrectly used commas: 12, 15, 16, 20
21. 'Why can't I tie this knot properly?' muttered Jim.
22. 'Look out!' warned Anastasia.
23. 'Which of these should I wear?' asked Danielle.
24. 'Land ahoy!' screamed the ship's watch.
25. 'Matt – why are you asking Amy?' enquired the teacher.
26. 'Ow! That hurt!' complained Jade.
27. 'Is that you, Aaron?' asked Shemar.
28. The Maths teacher yelled, 'Don't touch that, Dylan!'
29. 'Rebecca! You're amazing!' gushed her boyfriend.
30. 'Where is your homework?' said the teacher to Habib.
31. 'Lucy! No!' raged the team manager.
32. Stephan asked, 'How did you manage to work that out?'
33. 'Did your photographs come out OK?' remarked Kamal.
34. 'Watch my fingers!' warned Megan.
35. Bill shouted, 'You're fired!'
36. 'Why am I fired?' asked Dean.
37. 'Because of all the mistakes you made!' retorted Bill, angrily.
38. 'Why didn't you sack the others who made mistakes?' replied Dean.
39. 'Listen to me!' screeched Bill.
40. 'Why should I listen to someone who shouts all the time?' muttered Dean as he left.

Test 15
1. abbreviation
2. accelerate
3. accompaniment, accessory
4. pebble
5. accommodation
6. scribble
7. stubborn
8. accomplished
9. eccentric
10. occasionally
11. tying
12. wearing
13. hopping
14. pulling
15. tugging
16. tripping
17. occurring
18. whispering
19. pinning
20. transmitting
21. address
20. fiddle
23. forbidden
24. puddle
25. affection
26. coffee
27. sufficient
28. beggar
29. luggage
30. toboggan
31. cellar
32. immediately
33. beginning
34. tennis
35. appetite
36. opponent
37. hurricane
38. quarry
39. essay
40. passport

Test 16
1. b
2. e
3. d
4. a
5. e
6. b
7. c
8. d
9. a
10. e

Test 17
1. a
2. e
3. d
4. b
5. c
6. a
7. d
8. b
9. e
10. b

Test 18
1. ✗
2. ✓
3. ✓
4. ✗
5. ✗
6. ✓
7. ✓
8. ✗
9. ✓
10. ✓
11–20. Onomatopoeia: 11, 15, 17, 18
Personification: 12, 13, 14, 16, 19, 20
21. repetition
22. assonance
23. rhyme
24. rhyme
25. repetition
26. assonance
27. alliteration
28. assonance
29. repetition
30. assonance
31. simile
32. metaphor

33. personification   34. alliteration
35. onomatopoeia   36. assonance
37. alliteration   38. rhyme
39. simile   40. personification

Test 19
1. hadn't   2. wouldn't
3. isn't   4. I'm
5. You'll   6. should've
7. you're   8. They're
9. can't   10. I'd
11. the cat's tail
12. the children's coats
13. the ladies' handbags
14. the candles' flames
15. the people's votes
16. the ballerinas' dresses
17. the captain's hat
18. the Chancellor's briefcase
19. Emile's boots
20. the gentlemen's guild
21–25. Correctly used: 21, 24, 25
    Incorrectly used: 22, 23
26–50. Some commas, full stops and exclamation marks are
    interchangeable in this passage but the positioning is important.
    "I don't like the clowns," cried Lizzie as she sat by the circus ring.
    "They are trying to be funny and make you laugh," comforted
    Gran, who had thought that a trip to the circus would be a special
    treat for her youngest granddaughter.
    Looking worried, Lizzie explained, "It's their faces that scare me.
    You can't see who they are."
    "Look, here come the horses and their riders!" enthused Gran,
    pointing at the swaying curtains and trying to reassure her by
    changing the subject. "Don't they look amazing, Lizzie? I love their
    bridles!"
    Lizzie was smiling now and obviously enjoying this act.
    "Would you like an ice-cream, love?" enquired Gran.
    "Please can I have a choc ice?" asked Lizzie.
    "Of course," said Gran. "They are coming around with them during
    the interval."

Test 20
1. e   2. b
3. c   4. d
5. d   6. e
7. c   8. a
9. a   10. b

Test 21
1. c   2. a
3. b   4. e
5. a   6. e
7. b   8. c
9. c   10. b

Test 22
1. verb   2. preposition of place
3. adverb   4. abstract noun
5. collective noun   6. definite article
7. noun   8. proper noun
9. preposition of time   10. indefinite article
11. Running   12. Going
13. Hopping   14. Pining
15. Camping
Answers to 16–25 might include:
16. There was no traffic on the roads when I walked home.
17. Two squirrels with fluffy tails were balancing along the fence.
18. Waiting until sunset, the elephants visited the watering hole.
19. The baby hyenas were chased back to their tree trunk den by
    baboons.
20. Jake located the treasure, tracing the route with his finger.
21. Across the dirt tracks were webs spun by golden orb spiders.
22. In the Western Ghats, hornbills are often found.
23. Searching for a suitable tree, the bush baby leapt into the air.
24. Hippopotamuses are very graceful creatures under the water.
25. Kangaroos' pouches are very elastic.

Test 23
1. unnecessary
2. immature
3. disrespect
4. unhappy
5. inconspicuous
6. unclear
7. disconnect
8. irregular
9. disobey
10. imprecise
11. disbelief, unbelief
12. antiseptic, aseptic
13. non-violent
14. unable
15. unload
16. discomfort
17. dissatisfied
18. unsuitable
19. anticlimax
20. disarm
21. agreement
22. action, actor
23. server, servant, service
24. formula, formation, formulation, former are some of the possible
    answers
25. informer, information, informant
26. creation, creator
27. encouragement
28. living, livestock
29. implication
30. borrower
31. childish, childlike
32. amazing
33. reasonable
34. beautiful, beauteous
35. famous
36. spotty, spotted, spotless
37. economic, economical
38. useful, useless
39. considerate, considerable
40. revolutionary
41–50. The young man was in considerable **discomfort** after his **bicycle**
    ride for the transatlantic team. The mudguard **protector** had
    become detached and had **interfered** with the chain, causing him
    to dismount. While the bike was **stationary** he undertook some
    minor **adjustments**. **Unwilling** to give up, he quickly **remounted**
    the bike and **carefully** pushed off to test the running of the gears.
    Amazingly, he was back in the race.

Test 24
1. e   2. e
3. a   4. d
5. d   6. b
7. d   8. c
9. e   10. c

Test 25
1. c   2. b
3. d   4. e
5. c   6. b
7. a   8. d
9. b   10. c

Test 26
1–10. Correct agreement: 2, 4, 8, 10
    Incorrect agreement: 1, 3, 5, 6, 7, 9
11. stood   12. rode
13. had   14. sang
15. knitted
16. Both school football teams were losing at half time.
17. Liam wore fancy dress costumes at parties.
18. Isaac smiled a lot, especially when he concentrated.
19. Puna walked into the classroom when she was ready.
20. Maisie enjoyed school holidays because she could lie in.

21–30. The knight **approaches**. When young he always **dreamt** of jousting at court. He raises his lance. He remembers **his** father's advice, 'stay strong, don't falter'. The princess waves, dropping **her** handkerchief and his heart **leaps**. The joust **begins**. Everything Gawain has **learnt** is now focused on the **tournament** ahead. Now, **approaching** the tilt he accelerates, training his sight on the Black **Knight**.

Test 27

1. The Year 6 residential trip children needed to pack: a towel, two T-shirts, trousers and shoes.
2. Mum bought a lilac hat; her outfit for the wedding was pale violet.
3. Aladdin: (whispering to the audience) He's no idea who I am!
4. It was 16:00 when the final bell rang and the school finished for the day.
5. The squire gathered the knight's equipment: his lance, his helmet and his chain mail.
6. Her shopping list included: three packets of washing powder; a new washing line; a bag of pegs and a laundry basket.
7. Passage 18:11 from the Gospel according to Saint Mark was the vicar's favourite.
8. Dad watched the cricket on Sunday afternoon; it was his way of relaxing.
9. The dinner began with the toastmaster's call: 'Dinner is served'.
10. Marek bought a new fantasy adventure game; he was bored with all of his old adventure games.
11. My sister (stroppy, spotty, sixteen) spends all her time in her bedroom.
12. Cynthia: (entering from stage, left) I've found my handbag!
13. Janie had a new dog (lively, snappy, disobedient) just like her!
14. Uncle Percy (he was always late) screeched into the driveway and flung the door open.
15. Haresh: That's my final word! (Storms off into the crowd.)
16. Time passed... Jane could not remember what had happened.
17. 'I'm not sure...' There was an ominous pause before Jamil continued.
18. There was a gap in the text... what could it mean?
19. '... and winning medals,' continued the Prime Minister, 'is the name of the game.'
20. The cowboys waited... it wouldn't be long now.
21–25. Correctly used: 21, 23
    Incorrectly used: 22, 24, 25 (in question 24 the position is correct but the punctuation should be a hyphen)
26. To err is human; to forgive, divine.
27. Extra subjects were added to the timetable: history, geography and maths.
28. The Sun went down... the next thing he knew it was midday.
29. The Doctor: I will return with your prescription tomorrow.
30. She had worked hard: now she was ready for the exam.
31. Miss Blunt (young, pretty, new) was allocated Reception class B.
32. The old man waved his finger knowingly, 'Wait and see...'.
33. The School Council had a packed agenda: the toilets, the PE shed, the new school uniform.
34. 'Children are the future...' began the politician, getting fired up.
35. They went on every ride – even though they were tired – before they left the theme park.

Test 28

1.	excepted	2.	adapted
3.	allusion	4.	Always
5.	bare	6.	border
7.	coarse	8.	industrial
9.	pray	10.	morale
11.	accepted	12.	adopted
13.	illusion	14.	All ways
15.	bear	16.	boarder
17.	course	18.	industrious
19.	prey	20.	moral
21.	alcohol	22.	appearance
23.	eighth	24.	beautiful
25.	business	26.	cemetery
27.	committee	28.	friends
29.	received	30.	laboratory
31.	loneliness	32.	marriage
33.	necessary	34.	neighbour
35.	pursue	36.	scissors
37.	sentence	38.	soldier
39.	weird	40.	villain

Test 14: Commas, question marks and exclamation marks

Insert the missing **question marks**, **exclamation marks** and **full stops** into these sentences.

21. 'Why can't I tie this knot properly ' muttered Jim

22. 'Look out ' warned Anastasia

23. 'Which of these should I wear ' asked Danielle

24. 'Land ahoy ' screamed the ship's watch

25. 'Matt – why are you asking Amy ' enquired the teacher

26. 'Ow! That hurt ' complained Jade

27. 'Is that you, Aaron ' asked Shemar

28. The Maths teacher yelled, ' Don't touch that, Dylan '

29. 'Rebecca! You're amazing ' gushed her boyfriend

30. 'Where is your homework ' said the teacher to Habib

31. 'Lucy! No ' raged the team manager

32. Stephan asked, 'How did you manage to work that out '

33. 'Did your photographs come out OK ' remarked Kamal

34. 'Watch my fingers ' warned Megan

35. Bill shouted, ' You're fired '

36. 'Why am I fired ' asked Dean

37. 'Because of all the mistakes you made ' retorted Bill, angrily

38. 'Why didn't you sack the others who made mistakes ' replied Dean

39. 'Listen to me ' screeched Bill

40. 'Why should I listen to someone who shouts all the time ' muttered Dean as he left

/40

Test 15: Doubling letters

All of the missing words below have a double *b* or double *c* in them. Complete the sentences so that they make sense.

1. An **a**_____ is a shortened form of a word.

2. To increase speed is to **a**_____.

3. An extra item that often complements a main object is an **a**_____.

4. A **p**_____ is a hard stone, often smooth to the touch.

5. A place in which to live or stay is called **a**_____.

6. If you **s**_____, you don't write very tidily.

7. If you are **s**_____, it means you won't change your mind easily.

8. When you have achieved something you say that it has been **a**_____.

9. If someone or something is a bit unusual and quirky, it is described as
   e_____.

10. When something happens, but not very often, we say it happens **o**_____.

Add *ing* to the **verbs** in bold to complete the following sentences, making sure that they are spelt correctly.

11. The parcels needed **tie** _____ with string.

12. Ellie was **wear** _____ her favourite shoes.

13. After hurting her leg, Hannah went **hop** _____ to the changing rooms.

14. The cat was **pull** _____ the mouse by its tail.

15. The puppy was **tug** _____ the blanket

16. Be careful of **trip** _____ over the step!

17. The eclipse was **occur** _____ on Friday at midday.

18. The children were **whisper** _____ about the dreadful homework.

19. Jacinta spent the evening **pin** _____ up her new jeans.

20. The aliens were **transmit** _____ signals to Earth.

Complete these sentences with words containing a double *d, f* or *g*.

21. The name, or number, of the place where someone lives is their **a**_____.

22. A common name for a violin – it also means to cheat – is a **f**_____.

23. Something you are not allowed to do is **f**_____.

24. Water formed in a small hollow in the ground is a **p**_____.

25. A feeling similar to love is **a**_____.

26. A drink that usually contains caffeine and can be instant or made from beans is

    c_____.

27. When something is enough, it is **s**_____.

28. A person who asks for money is a **b**_____.

29. Items that you take with you on holiday or on a journey are called **l**_____.

30. A kind of sledge is a **t**_____.

Complete these sentences with words containing a double letter.

31. A place under a building, often used for storage is a **c**_____.

32. Straight away – **i**_____.

33. The start of something is the **b**_____.

34. A sport involving rackets, sometimes played on grass, is called **t**_____.

35. The desire for something, usually associated with food, is an **a**_____.

36. The person you compete against is an **o**_____.

37. An extremely strong wind, usually found in the tropics, is a **h**_____.

38. A place from where raw materials are dug from the ground is a **q**_____.

39. A name given for an extended piece of writing is an **e**_____.

40. A document needed to gain entry to a country is called a **p**_____.

/40

Read the poem below and then answer the questions that follow.

Going home

1 Click, click, click, the combination
Stow the books in preparation,
Everything secured in place
Hi-Vis jacket – just in case,
Crank to set the wheels in motion
Sprocket moves... proceed with caution.

2 Look both ways then join the traffic,
Honking horns... a bit dramatic!
Freewheel through the old arcade
Over asphalt freshly laid,
Mind the puddles by the theatre,
Oops, I think I splashed a teacher!

3 Bump, bump, bump along the cobbles
Hold on tight, no time to wobble,
Overtake the Number 10
Hit the brakes, then round the bend,
Panniers thud into the saddle
Steady now and grip the handles.

4 Whir and clank the chain is catching
Gears are grinding, rubbers snatching
Drive on up the final rise
Sinews strain and muscles cry
Just one more push, accelerate,
It's dinner time, I can't be late!

1. How many surfaces are mentioned in the poem?

   a) 1   **b)** 2   **c)** 3   **d)** 4   **e)** 5

2. Which two of these items are not parts of the poet's bike?

   1 sprocket   **2** horn   **3** wheels   **4** sinews   **5** gears

   a) 1 and 2   **b)** 2 and 3   **c)** 3 and 5   **d)** 4 and 5   **e)** 2 and 4

3. Why does the rider freewheel through the arcade?

   a) to rush home for dinner   **b)** to avoid the pedestrians

   c) to avoid the bus   **d)** because the surface is smooth

   e) because it's by the theatre

4. Which of these is not a problem in stanza 4?

    a) bumpy road surface

    b) painful legs

    c) being late

    d) brakes catching on the wheels

    e) faulty drive chain

5. What type of figurative language is 'muscles cry' in stanza 4?

    a) alliteration   **b)** onomatopoeia   **c)** assonance

    d) simile   **e)** personification

6. What type of figurative language is used on the first line of stanzas 1, 3 and 4?

    a) alliteration   **b)** onomatopoeia   **c)** assonance

    d) repetition   **e)** personification

7. What is the syllable pattern in each verse?

    a) 5, 5, 4, 4, 5, 5   **b)** 8, 8, 8, 8, 8, 8   **c)** 8, 8, 7, 7, 8, 8

    d) 7, 7, 7, 7, 7, 7   **e)** 5, 5, 7, 7, 5, 5

8. What is the rhyming pattern of the poem?

    a) A, A, B, B, A, A   **b)** A, B, C, A, B, C   **c)** A, B, A, B, A, B

    d) A, A, B, B, C, C   **e)** A, B, B, C, C, A

9. What is the most likely location for this poem?

    a) a city   **b)** a village   **c)** a new town

    d) an industrial estate   **e)** a campus

10. What is clicking in stanza 1?

    a) pedals   **b)** gears   **c)** sprockets

    d) jacket   **e)** lock

/10

Read the text below and then answer the questions that follow.

Satellites

Since the 1950s, man has been sending satellites into orbit around the Earth to collect information and help us to communicate with each other and, although we can't see them, we receive the benefits of their presence every day. These satellites mostly fall into three main categories: weather, communication and military, which are, in turn, split into different types according to their specific function.

Weather satellites
Meteorologists use two different kinds of satellite to follow weather systems: polar-orbiting satellites and geostationary satellites.

Polar-orbiting satellites provide general research data such as temperature and humidity and are located about 850km above the Earth, orbiting the globe roughly every 100 minutes. They can also be useful for search and rescue as they carry specific transponders, which help to locate aircraft that have crashed or ships in distress.

Geostationary satellites provide the images for television weather forecasts and can be used for tracking destructive hurricanes and tropical storms. They are located high above the equator (around 36 000km) and revolve in the same direction as the Earth, one orbit taking 24 hours. A single satellite can see about 40 per cent of the Earth's surface, so three of these devices can cover the entire planet, apart from small areas at the North and South Poles.

Communication satellites
Satellites used to track and transmit communications are called COMSATs. These also fall into two main types: low Earth-orbiting and direct broadcast. Because Earth-orbiting satellites can only see any given part of the Earth for a short time, a large number are needed to cover a relatively small area. Direct broadcast satellites are particularly high-powered and transmit to small satellite dishes, such as the type that receive domestic television signals.

Military satellites
This third category of satellite is used by governments for surveillance purposes. These devices are used to provide information such as where there is a lot of activity on air bases and to find out whether a particular country is developing more weapons. Because these satellites are top secret nobody really knows how many there are.

Since 1957, the United States Space Surveillance Network (SSN) has tracked over 24 500 objects orbiting Earth, most of which have become unstable over time and burnt up in the Earth's atmosphere. There were roughly 8000 satellites travelling around the Earth in 2012, yet just 3000 of these were operational. In other words, over 60 per cent of the satellites orbiting the Earth are junk!

1. Which kind of satellite would be best suited to track down a crashed helicopter?
   a) polar-orbiting satellite   **b)** geostationary satellite   **c)** low-orbiting COMSAT
   d) direct broadcast COMSAT   **e)** military satellite

2. What kind of satellite would be used to collect intelligence information?
   a) polar-orbiting satellite   b) geostationary satellite   c) low-orbiting COMSAT
   d) direct broadcast COMSAT   e) military satellite

3. Approximately how many satellites are believed to be functional in 2012?
   a) 24 500   b) 8000   c) 60 per cent   d) 3000   e) 1957

4. Which of these statements is true, according to the text?
   a) Geostationary satellites are located above the North and South Poles.
   b) COMSATs are used to track and transmit communications.
   c) Military satellites are used to locate ships in distress.
   d) There are 24 500 military satellites.
   e) Direct broadcast satellites are very low powered.

5. Which of these words is closest in meaning to 'benefits' as it appears in the first paragraph?
   a) social security   b) disadvantages   c) advantages
   d) communications   e) information

6. Why have there been campaigns to clean up space?
   a) There are many redundant space objects.   b) All satellites are junk.
   c) Satellites only last 20 years.   d) Communication satellites block Internet signals.
   e) Satellites hamper rescue operations.

7. Which of these is closest to the description 'for surveillance purposes'?
   a) to watch dolphins   b) to survey weather systems   c) to cover up secret activities
   d) to monitor activity   e) none of the above

8. What type of language feature is 'SSN' in the final paragraph?
   a) mnemonic   b) acronym   c) abbreviation   d) synonym   e) proper noun

9. For how long have satellites been helping us to communicate?
   a) 100 minutes   b) 24 hours   c) less than 50 years
   d) over 60 per cent   e) less than 70 years

10. In which section is information about the distance satellites orbit above the Earth?
    a) introduction   b) weather satellites   c) communication satellites
    d) military satellites   e) none of these

/10

Tick the sentences that are correctly labelled as **simile** or **metaphor**.

1. The bare trees stretched out towards the horizon like ghosts. **Metaphor**

2. Water trickled down stalactites like frozen icicles in the underground cavern. **Simile**

3. Chandelier earrings and a silk gown completed the outfit for the ball. **Metaphor**

4. The waterfall sound of their laughter cascaded through the air. **Simile**

5. His smile lingered like that of the Cheshire Cat. **Metaphor**

6. His face crumpled like an empty paper bag. **Simile**

7. Lion-hearted soldiers faced the advancing troops. **Metaphor**

8. Ballerina flowers danced across the forest floor. **Simile**

9. Regimented houses lined the main road. **Metaphor**

10. Shaking like a leaf, the girl approached the examiner. **Simile**

List the examples of **onomatopoeia** and **personification** from the text in the table below.

'**Brring, brring**',(11) the alarm clock **shouted (12)** at Ajit, **urging (13)** him to wake up. The curtains flapped, trying to **grab (14)** his attention. **Bang**! (15) The front door slammed, **telling (16)** him that Dad had left for work. But still he slept on, trying to ignore the signs that the morning had begun. '**Meow**', (17) **purred (18)** the cat. It was hungry and nobody seemed to be available to feed it. The bed springs **moaned (19)** as Ajit slowly sat up, avoiding the persistent noise coming from the small creature desperate to be fed. The smell of toast **called (20)** from the stairwell. Mum was making breakfast.

Onomatopoeia	Personification

Write on the answer lines whether each example includes **alliteration**, **assonance**, **repetition** or **rhyme**.

21. I came, I saw, I conquered. _____

22. The farthest star was alarmingly bright. _____

23. The fake snake was definitely a mistake. _____

24. Beware of the chair that needs some repair! _____

25. A dark tree shook, in a dark forest, in the dark country. _____

26. Dining time for the king tiger. _____

27. The knight was fed up with the jumping jolly jester. _____

28. The spiders hid in the linen basket. _____

29. The case was closed and the judge's mind was closed. _____

30. The cold wind blows and the children's noses and toes become frozen. _____

Identify the type of figurative language used in each sentence.

31. The cricket balls were covered in spiders' webs like strange cocoons. _____

32. Toadstool umbrellas covered the grass around the bandstand. _____

33. The top of the climbing wall beckoned the young climber. _____

34. The marvellous music could be heard from the apothecary's arboretum. _____

35. Splash! Owen groaned as his trainer sank below the water. _____

36. Finding the line of string was all that Theseus could think of. _____

37. It was amazing and awesome; Dom was certain he could do it. _____

38. 'You may have been first, but your style was the worst!' he sneered. _____

39. 'Dance like a puppet on a string,' laughed the small girl. _____

40. The comfy sofa kept calling Mum as she tried to get the baby off to sleep. _____

/40

Test 19: Apostrophes and speech marks

> Replace the words in bold with the shortened version.

Example: Anna **could not** <u>couldn't</u> swim.

1. Daryl **had not** _____ seen the new film at the cinema.

2. Under the new scheme, Jules **would not** _____ get his usual tickets.

3. 'This **is not** _____ going the way I had hoped,' laughed Pedro.

4. 'I am _____ too hot today; it is over 32 degrees,' commented Gerald.

5. 'You will _____ always remember this rhyme,' remarked Miss James.

6. 'I should have _____ taken my umbrella to the concert,' Mum complained.

7. Never underestimate your opponent, **you are** _____ bound to lose if you do.

8. **They are** _____ getting closer to winning every time they play.

9. I **cannot** _____ go to the gym this week.

10. I **had** _____ no plans to return.

> Rewrite the phrase to show the **apostrophe of possession**.

Example: the shoes that are owned by Jane   <u>Jane's shoes</u>

11. the tail of the cat   _____

12. the coats belonging to the children   _____

13. the handbags owned by the ladies   _____

14. the flames of the candles   _____

15. the votes of the people   _____

16. the dresses of the ballerinas   _____

17. the hat bought by the captain   _____

18. the briefcase possessed by the Chancellor   _____

19. the boot belonging to Emile   _____

20. the guild of the gentlemen   _____

Tick the columns in the chart to indicate whether
the **apostrophes** are correctly used in each sentence.

Sentence	Correctly used	Incorrectly used
21. **It's** going to be a late start tomorrow.		
22. The lion waved **it's** tail majestically.		
23. The ant carried **it's** leaf back to the nest.		
24. **It's** up to you now you've completed the revision.		
25. Jamil shouted, '**It's** not fair!'		

Add the missing **punctuation** and **speech marks** to this passage.

26–50. I don't like the clowns cried Lizzie as she sat by the circus ring.

They are trying to be funny and make you laugh comforted Gran, who had thought that a trip to the circus would be a special treat for her youngest granddaughter.

Looking worried, Lizzie explained, It's their faces that scare me. You can't see who they are.

Look, here come the horses and their riders enthused Gran, pointing at the swaying curtains and trying to reassure her by changing the subject. Don't they look amazing, Lizzie I love their bridles

Lizzie was smiling now and obviously enjoying this act.

Would you like an ice-cream, love enquired Gran.

Please can I have a choc ice? asked Lizzie.

Of course, said Gran. They are coming around with them during the interval

/50

Read the text below and then answer the questions that follow.

Yggdrasil, the Tree of Life

1 Long ago, in the time of the Vikings, poets told tales of a giant ash tree which held nine worlds in its vast canopy. The branches of this great tree stretched high into the heavens and the three gargantuan roots that supported it reached into faraway lands, drinking from three magic wells.

2 The first well was the source of all cold rivers and lay under the kingdom of Hel, the land of the dead. This land was inhabited by Nidhogg, an evil dragon which gnawed into the tree's flesh, rotting it away. At the end of the second great root lay Mimir's well, the Well of Wisdom. Frost giants were said to dwell beneath this second root so travelling through this kingdom was fraught with danger.

3 The final root drank from the Well of Fate, which was protected by three maidens who created the laws of mankind and decided their destiny. These maidens nurtured Yggdrasil using mud from the well, frustrating the dragon's attempts to destroy it. The source of the third well was in the heavens, ruled by the god Odin, and below which dwelt the kingdom of mankind.

4 Although Odin was very powerful, he also longed to rule over the nine worlds in the tree. To do this he knew he would have to find the magic runes hidden in each kingdom. So one day, knowing that he faced almost certain death, he set off to retrieve them.

5 Piercing himself with his own spear, Odin offered himself as a sacrifice to Yggdrasil and hung there for nine days and nine nights. Ravaged by thirst and hunger, he was taunted by Ratatosk the squirrel who lived in the tree and gradually grew weaker and weaker.

6 Finally, when he could take no more, the exhausted god fell from the tree, catching the runes as he fell. Odin's sacrifice had been rewarded and he clutched the wisdom of all nine kingdoms in his hands.

1. What was used to maintain the third root?

   a) water   b) canopy   c) Nidhogg   d) frost giants   e) mud

2. What or who goads Odin?

   a) the maidens protecting the well   b) Ratatosk
   c) the dragon   d) the tree
   e) the poets

3. Why was Odin's sacrifice rewarded?

  a) he was very powerful

  b) he dwelt in the kingdom of mankind

  c) he offered himself as a sacrifice

  d) an evil dragon gnawed the tree's flesh

  e) he fought the frost giants

4. Who dwelt around the tree roots?

  1 Yggdrasil   **2** Nidhogg   **3** maidens   **4** Ratatosk   **5** frost giants

  a) 1, 3 and 5   **b)** 2, 3 and 4   **c)** 1, 3 and 4

  d) 2, 3 and 5   **e)** 3, 4 and 5

5. Which paragraph explains Odin's aspirations?

  a) 1   **b)** 2   **c)** 3   **d)** 4   **e)** 5

6. What does 'gargantuan' mean?

  a) green   **b)** gallant   **c)** grafted   **d)** fibrous   **e)** colossal

7. Which adjective could not be used to describe Odin?

  a) powerful   **b)** thirsty   **c)** humorous   **d)** exhausted   **e)** rewarded

8. What is the moral of this story?

  a) No pain, no gain.

  b) Many hands make light work.

  c) A bird in the hand is worth two in the bush.

  d) Mighty oaks from little acorns grow.

  e) Money doesn't grow on trees.

9. Which characters (or character) mentioned in the text indicate that this is a myth rather than a legend?

  a) the god, Odin   **b)** the Vikings   **c)** the poets

  d) the maidens   **e)** mankind

10. What is the name for these word types?

  tales/tails   root/route   weak/week

  a) adjectives   **b)** homophones   **c)** antonyms

  d) pseudonyms   **e)** homographs

/10

Read the text below and then answer the questions that follow.

Are compulsory PE lessons a breach of children's human rights?

1 Children are surrounded today by every temptation to sit in front of a screen, whether it be a television, games console or a computer to do their homework. This trend has led to a sedentary culture in young people which, although they are often blamed for it, is more the fault of the adults around them. Compulsory PE is the only antidote we currently have for this failing of the country's children and removing it would be a dangerous step.

2 Laziness and boredom are classic symptoms of an unhealthy child. This lack of motivation affects both their happiness and their ability to succeed as the competitive drive to win, learnt through sport, is vital for their adult life. The world of work revolves around competition: for jobs, for promotions and for bonuses. So are we to deprive children of the opportunity to be the best that they can be?

3 Furthermore, bored, inactive children tend to eat and we are all familiar with the news reports about how obesity and Type 2 diabetes in young people is on the increase. But despite these figures, there are still parents prepared to indulge their offspring in the erroneous name of safety. It is often said that the roads are too dangerous for children to cycle on, yet recent statistics detail less than 120 deaths annually from cycling and around 85 000 deaths from cancer and coronary heart disease relating to inactivity.

4 Although these figures speak for themselves, there are still many ambitious parents who think PE takes away valuable time from academic lessons. However, many studies have shown that the areas of the brain that are stimulated through exercise are associated with memory and learning, so children deprived of exercise are conversely less likely to learn effectively.

5 An additional benefit of PE is that it teaches children to collaborate with others. Team sports encourage children to work together for a positive end and this not only leads to success on the field but equips them for life both at work and in the wider community.

6 Do I think children's rights are compromised by being forced to take exercise in schools? I think their human rights would be compromised if PE was not compulsory because they would be ill-equipped to develop into fruitful, fit and fulfilled members of society.

1. What excuse do parents use for not allowing their children to cycle?
   a) recent statistics
   b) to raise academic standards
   c) the roads are unsafe
   d) there is a risk of cancer
   e) they might get Type 2 diabetes

2. What affect does exercise have on the brain, according to research?
   a) improves thought processes
   b) encourages eating
   c) leads to risk-taking
   d) helps children to work together
   e) produces fulfilled members of society

3. Why does the author use statistics?
   a) to show cycling is dangerous
   b) to show lack of exercise has health risks
   c) to show she's done a lot of research
   d) to reassure ambitious parents
   e) to persuade us that PE is optional

4. What does competition help children to attain, according to the text?
   1 boredom   2 jobs   3 promotion   4 bonuses   5 obesity
   a) 1, 3, 5   b) 1, 2, 3   c) 3, 4, 5   d) 1, 3, 4   e) 2, 3, 4

5. Which of these comments best reflects the writer's viewpoint?
   a) Compulsory PE develops a successful workforce.
   b) Forced PE lessons are inhuman.
   c) PE does not develop children's academic potential.
   d) We need more workers, not more sportsmen.
   e) Children collaborating as teams leads to a gang culture.

6. What type of language is 'although these figures speak for themselves'?
   a) metaphor   b) onomatopoeia   c) proverb   d) synonym   e) personification

7. Who does this article say is responsible for the lack of exercise in young people?
   a) the government   b) parents   c) sports organisations
   d) the world of work   e) members of society

8. In what type of publication would you be likely to find this text?
   a) an encyclopedia   b) a gossip magazine   c) a tabloid newspaper
   d) a directory   e) a biography

9. Which words in the text suggest that children are couch potatoes?
   1 sedentary   2 erroneous   3 stimulated   4 inactive   5 compromised
   a) 1 and 2   b) 1 and 3   c) 1 and 4   d) 1 and 5   e) 2 and 3

10. What does the word 'antidote' suggest?
    a) PE is compulsory
    b) inactivity is a poison
    c) inactivity helps you succeed
    d) that parents indulge their offspring
    e) human rights would be compromised

/10

Identify the **parts of speech** with which each of these sentences begin.

Example: Before you call, decide what you want to say.   preposition of time

1. Leaping over the final hurdle, Jennifer caught her foot and
   lost the race.   _____

2. Under the new decking, a family of rats was busily
   making a nest.   _____

3. Surprisingly, there were 10 puppies in the litter.   _____

4. Laughter filled the theatre when the actor hid behind
   the curtain.   _____

5. Herds of buffalo migrated across the African plains.   _____

6. The snow dusted the shrubs at the end of the garden.   _____

7. Yesterday started badly when I forgot my homework.   _____

8. Cambridge is famous for its university.   _____

9. Until you have signed the documents, the computer
   is not yours.   _____

10. A tarantula is an exotic species of spider.   _____

Use the **verb** at the end of each line to complete these sentences.

11. _____ to the bus stop, he fell over.   **to run**

12. _____ to the gymkhana, they had a really good time, for once.   **to go**

13. _____ from lilypad to lilypad, the frog escaped from the heron.   **to hop**

14. _____ for her boyfriend, Sarah refused to go out.   **to pine**

15. _____ at the site, they all got soaked!   **to camp**

Test 22: Starting sentences

Rewrite these sentences beginning with the word at the end of each line (to replace the underlined word). You may need to adapt the text so that it makes sense.

16. When I walked home <u>there</u> was no traffic on the roads. **There**

_____

17. Balancing along the fence were <u>two</u> squirrels with fluffy tails. **Two**

_____

18. The elephants <u>waited</u> until sunset to visit the watering hole. **Waiting**

_____

19. Baboons chased <u>the</u> baby hyenas back to their tree trunk den. **The**

_____

20. Tracing the route with his finger, <u>Jake</u> located the treasure. **Jake**

_____

21. Golden orb spiders spun their webs <u>across</u> the dirt tracks. **Across**

_____

22. Hornbills are often found <u>in</u> the Western Ghats. **In**

_____

23. The bush baby <u>searched</u> for a suitable tree then leapt into the air. **Searching**

_____

24. Under the water <u>hippopotamuses</u> are very graceful creatures. **Hippopotamuses**

_____

25. The pouches of <u>kangaroos</u> are very elastic. **Kangaroos**

_____

/25

Test 23: Prefixes and suffixes

Add a **prefix** to all of these words to form a word with an opposite meaning.

1. necessary _____
2. mature _____
3. respect _____
4. happy _____
5. conspicuous _____
6. clear _____
7. connect _____
8. regular _____
9. obey _____
10. precise _____
11. belief _____
12. septic _____
13. violent _____
14. able _____
15. load _____
16. comfort _____
17. satisfied _____
18. suitable _____
19. climax _____
20. arm _____

Change these verbs into nouns by adding a **suffix**. Some may have more than one possible answer. You may need to change some letters in the original word.

Example: argue   **argument**

21. agree _____
22. act _____
23. serve _____
24. form _____
25. inform _____
26. create _____
27. encourage _____
28. live _____
29. imply _____
30. borrow _____

Add **suffixes** to these words to turn them into adjectives. Some may have more than one possible answer.

31. child _____

32. amaze _____

33. reason _____

34. beauty _____

35. fame _____

36. spot _____

37. economy _____

38. use _____

39. consider _____

40. revolution _____

Read this passage and underline the misspelt words containing **prefixes** and **suffixes**.

41–50. The young man was in considerable disscomfort after his bycicle ride for the

transatlantic team. The mudguard protecter had become detached and had interferred

with the chain, causing him to dismount. While the bike was stationery he undertook

some minor adjustmants. Unwiling to give up, he quickly remmounted the bike

and carefuly pushed off to test the running of the gears. Amazeingly, he was back

in the race.

/50

Read the letter below and then answer the questions that follow.

Jeremy Sutton
65 Market Street
Saffron Waters
Essex
CB12 5TU

Customer Services
Supercool Sports
Leytonbridge
London EC10 5LW

1 August 2013

Re:

Dear Sir or Madam,

On June 21st 2013 I ordered a new pair of rugby boots priced at £23.99 (item 22-33-4451 from your catalogue) and received the order on June 26th. Unfortunately, when I opened the box, I saw that the boots you had sent me were both for the right foot.

As the boots were needed for a tournament the following weekend, I called your efficient helpline immediately and they agreed to send me a replacement pair, asking that I use your reply-paid sticker to return the boots I had already received. I sent the parcel the following day and received your parcel the day after.

Having ordered from your catalogue before, I anticipated that my account would be refunded within the week for the initial purchase, as I believe is your policy. However, when I checked my statement today (see enclosed) five weeks after the return of the goods, it appears that I have been charged for both pairs.

As a valued customer, I am sure you will seek to rectify this oversight as soon as possible and credit me with the £23.99 for the original boots. I would also appreciate it if you could acknowledge receipt of this letter immediately and then delete my credit card details from your system.

Thank you in advance for dealing with this matter. I have been a satisfied customer of your company for many years and this is the first time I have encountered any problems. Should you need to contact me, I can be reached on (01998) 556743 at any time during working hours.

Yours faithfully,
Jeremy Sutton
Jeremy Sutton
Enc.

Test 24: Letter writing

1. At what time can Jeremy Sutton be contacted?
   - **a)** in the morning
   - **b)** in the afternoon
   - **c)** between 06:00 and 11:00
   - **d)** between 16:00 and 22:00
   - **e)** between 09:00 and 17:00

2. When was the second parcel received by Jeremy Sutton?
   - **a)** 1st August
   - **b)** 21st June
   - **c)** 26th June
   - **d)** 27th June
   - **e)** 28th June

3. What is the main reason for the letter of complaint?
   - **a)** he has not received a refund
   - **b)** he has received two boots for his right foot
   - **c)** there has been a delay in sending a replacement
   - **d)** the boots cost £23.99
   - **e)** he is a satisfied customer

4. What else, apart from the letter, would Customer Services expect to find in the envelope?
   - **a)** credit card details
   - **b)** a reply-paid sticker
   - **c)** a new catalogue
   - **d)** a credit card statement
   - **e)** football boots

5. What would you expect the company's initial response to be?
   - **a)** to send a new pair of boots
   - **b)** to send two left feet
   - **c)** to refund the postage
   - **d)** to let Jeremy know his letter has arrived
   - **e)** to return his credit card

6. What standard information is missing from this letter?
   - **a)** bank details
   - **b)** reference
   - **c)** customer services telephone number
   - **d)** post code
   - **e)** enclosure

7. Which adjectives in the letter suggest Jeremy is a previously happy customer?
   1 replacement **2** anticipated **3** initial **4** efficient **5** satisfied
   - **a)** 1 and 2
   - **b)** 2 and 3
   - **c)** 3 and 4
   - **d)** 4 and 5
   - **e)** 2 and 5

8. In what order do these events happen according to the letter?
   1 letter written **2** looked at catalogue **3** boots returned
   4 statement checked **5** boots ordered
   - **a)** 5, 3, 1, 2, 4
   - **b)** 1, 2, 3, 4, 5
   - **c)** 2, 5, 3, 4, 1
   - **d)** 5, 4, 3, 2, 1
   - **e)** 1, 3, 5, 2, 4

9. Which of these is not necessarily a feature of a formal letter?
   - **a)** salutation 'Dear Sir or Madam'
   - **b)** signature
   - **c)** ending 'Yours faithfully'
   - **d)** reference
   - **e)** an enclosure

10. Why has Jeremy not signed his letter 'Yours sincerely'?
    - **a)** it is a formal letter
    - **b)** it is an informal letter
    - **c)** he does not know the name of the addressee
    - **d)** he knows the name of the addressee
    - **e)** he is not happy with the service he has received

/10

Read the text below and then answer the questions that follow.

King Kieran spurred on to victory

1   On a rainy autumn day Kieran Delaney competed in his first wheelchair marathon in Dublin, the town of his birth. It was to be an emotional homecoming. Having left Ireland at 15 to realise his dream of being a jockey, Kieran's career was tragically cut short after a well-publicised fall in the April 2010 Grand National. After his accident at the notorious Becher's Brook, Kieran endured two and a half years of gruelling physiotherapy to prepare him for this big day.

2   During his recovery, Kieran became a familiar sight in the equestrian town of Newmarket, Suffolk where he undertook his daily training sessions using the long straight roads and bridle paths to build up stamina and muscle tone. His distinctive green wheelchair was a gift from a local Middle Eastern potentate in recognition of his many victories for the Danley stud, and it was often seen in the White Hart where he celebrated the successes of his fellow able-bodied jockeys.

3   Focused not only on his personal goals but also on supporting other paraplegics, Kieran was racing to raise money for the Injured Jockeys' Fund and Aspire, the spinal injuries charity. Aiming to complete the circuit in 2:50 he was understandably delighted to finish in 2:41 – well exceeding his personal best road-racing time.

4   Although Kieran had chosen slower tyres than his main competitors from Stoke Mandeville, this gave him an advantage in the wet weather. Danny Fletcher, army veteran and close friend of Kieran, was using a new Draft racing chair built for endurance, however his choice of tyres made him wary in the treacherous conditions.

5   When interviewed for Irish radio, Kieran said the most challenging part of the race was the section of the course between Terenure Road East and Milltown Road. Several people were being escorted to the St John's Ambulance first aid station and this 17-mile point seemed to be a critical distance for many of the participants.

6   'Turning the corner at Fosters Avenue by University College made me think of my wife who studied there,' Kieran recollected 'and her unfaltering support throughout my recuperation inspired me to draw on an inner strength and battle through the punctures for the final five miles.'

7   Congratulations, Kieran. We were all immensely proud of you!

1. Which location formed part of the most difficult section of the wheelchair marathon course?

   a) Fosters Avenue   **b)** University College   **c)** Terenure Road East

   d) Becher's Brook   **e)** Stoke Mandeville

2. What gave Kieran the upper hand in the race?

   a) his wheelchair   **b)** his tyres   **c)** the Middle Eastern potentate

   d) his training   **e)** the sponsors

3. How do we know Kieran isn't resentful of able-bodied jockeys?
   a) He raised money for the Injured Jockey's Fund.
   b) He supported other paraplegics.
   c) He lived in Newmarket, Suffolk.
   d) He celebrated with them in the pub.
   e) He focused on his personal goals.

4. When does Kieran's wheelchair marathon take place?
   a) April 2010   b) October 2010   c) April 2011
   d) October 2011   e) October 2012

5. What is the purpose of the quotation marks in paragraph 6?
   a) to indicate place names
   b) to show it was on the radio
   c) to separate the words Kieran recounts
   d) to indicate a chatty style
   e) to make it seem more realistic

6. Which of these words are used in the text to illustrate that the course was difficult?
   1 stamina   **2** wary   **3** treacherous   **4** gruelling   **5** emotional
   a) 1 and 2   b) 2 and 3   c) 3 and 4   d) 4 and 5   e) 1 and 4

7. What was the difference between Kieran's expected time and his actual time?
   a) 9 minutes faster   b) 9 minutes slower   c) 91 minutes faster
   d) 91 minutes slower   e) he equalled his record

8. Which publication would be unlikely to run this article?
   a) Dublin Evening News   b) Aspire annual report   c) The Suffolk Standard
   d) University College prospectus   e) Newmarket newsletter

9. Which word is closest in meaning to 'potentate'?
   a) country   b) leader   c) fashion designer   d) milliner   e) shop

10. Who is saying 'Congratulations, Kieran. We were all immensely proud of you!'?
    a) Danny Fletcher   b) Kieran's wife   c) the editorial team
    d) the writer   e) Danley stud

/10

Tick the columns in the chart to indicate whether the **verb** and **subject** agreement in these sentences is correct.

Sentence	Correct	Incorrect
The boys **are** playing football tonight.	✔	
1. Madison and her friends is going out.		
2. Olivia is changing her job.		
3. Nobody knew what Elijah were doing.		
4. Alyssa and Carlos are going to Leeds.		
5. The supermarket were opening a new branch.		
6. What was they thinking of?		
7. Alicia weren't happy.		
8. Kathryn and Tom were cleaning.		
9. Nobody knew that Judith were a secret agent!		
10. Jackson was getting ready.		

Change the verbs in bold into the **past tense** so that the sentences will still make sense.

Example: Mia **eats** broccoli.   <u>ate</u>

11. Miguel **stands** outside the school gates. _____

12. Samantha **rides** her horse.   _____

13. Alexandra **has** long hair.   _____

14. Robbie **sings** to himself, quietly.   _____

15. Jasmine **knits** socks for babies.   _____

Change these sentences from their current tense into the **past tense**, altering as few words as possible.

Example: Marie **is** eating fish and chewing vegetables at the same time.

Answer: Marie **was** eating fish and chewing vegetables at the same time.

16. Both school football teams are losing at half time.

_____

17. Liam wears fancy dress costumes at parties.

_____

18. Isaac smiles a lot, especially when he concentrates.

_____

19. Puna walks into the classroom when she is ready.

_____

20. Maisie enjoys school holidays because she can lie in.

_____

Complete the following passage using *all* the words from the box below.

her	his	begins	leaps	dreamt	approaching	approaches
Knight	tournament	learnt				

The knight **(21)** _____. When young he always **(22)** _____ of jousting at

court. He raises his lance. He remembers **(23)** _____ father's advice, 'stay strong,

don't falter'. The princess waves, dropping **(24)** _____ handkerchief and his heart

(25) _____. The joust **(26)** _____. Everything Gawain has **(27)**

_____ is now focused on the **(28)** _____ ahead. Now, **(29)**

_____ the tilt he accelerates, training his sight on the Black **(30)** _____.

/30

Test 27: Ellipses, dashes, colons, semicolons and brackets

> Insert either a colon or a semicolon into each of these sentences.
> All existing punctuation is in the correct place.

1. The Year 6 residential trip children needed to pack a towel, two T-shirts, trousers and shoes.
2. Mum bought a lilac hat her outfit for the wedding was pale violet.
3. Aladdin (whispering to the audience) He's no idea who I am!
4. It was 16 00 when the final bell rang and the school finished for the day.
5. The squire gathered the knight's equipment his lance, his helmet and his chain mail.
6. Her shopping list included: three packets of washing powder; a new washing line a bag of pegs and a laundry basket.
7. Passage 18 11 from the Gospel according to Saint Mark was the vicar's favourite.
8. Dad watched the cricket on Sunday afternoon it was his way of relaxing.
9. The dinner began with the toastmaster's call 'Dinner is served'.
10. Marek bought a new fantasy adventure game he was bored with all of his old adventure games.

> Insert **brackets** into the correct places in these sentences.

11. My sister stroppy, spotty, sixteen spends all her time in her bedroom.
12. Cynthia: entering from stage, left I've found my handbag!
13. Janie had a new dog lively, snappy, disobedient just like her!
14. Uncle Percy he was always late screeched into the driveway and flung the door open.
15. Haresh: That's my final word! Storms off into the crowd.

> Insert **ellipses** into the correct places in these sentences.

16. Time passed Jane could not remember what had happened .
17. ' I'm not sure ' There was an ominous pause before Jamil continued .
18. There was a gap in the text what could it mean ?
19. ' and winning medals, ' continued the Prime Minister ' is the name of the game . '
20. The cowboys waited it wouldn't be long now.

> Tick the columns on the chart to indicate whether the **dashes** are correctly used in each sentence.

Test 27: Ellipses, dashes, colons, semicolons and brackets

Sentence	Correctly used	Incorrectly used
21. They went shopping – despite the rain – as they needed uniforms.		
22. They lived happily – ever after or did they?		
23. The prize-giving was scheduled for 20:00–21:00.		
24. The boy had been press–ganged into volunteering.		
25. The highwayman – held up the coach would he get the jewels?		

> Insert **colons**, **semicolons** and **ellipses** into the correct places in these sentences.

26. To err is human to forgive , divine .
27. Extra subjects were added to the timetable history , geography and maths .
28. The Sun went down the next thing he knew it was midday .
29. The Doctor I will return with your prescription tomorrow .
30. She had worked hard now she was ready for the exam .

> These sentences include the correct punctuation marks. However, they are not all in the correct position. Rewrite each sentence correctly.

31. Miss Blunt young, pretty, new was allocated (Reception) class B.
   _____

32. The old man... waved his finger knowingly, 'Wait and see'.
   _____

33. The School Council: had a packed agenda the toilets, the PE shed, the new school uniform.
   _____

34. 'Children are the future' ...began the politician, getting fired up.
   _____

35. They – went on every ride even though they were tired before they left – the theme park.
   _____

/35

Underline the word that has been used incorrectly in each of these sentences.

1. The student excepted the award.

2. The child was adapted by his foster parents.

3. The magician performed an allusion that amazed everyone.

4. Always to the festival were blocked, because of an accident on the motorway.

5. The bare in the zoo looked rather fed up.

6. The landlord got rid of his new border because he wasn't paying his rent.

7. The race coarse was flooded, so the meeting couldn't go ahead.

8. The hard-working boy was described as industrial by his teachers.

9. The bird of pray circled over the dense woodlands.

10. The morale of the story is that you shouldn't cheat and look at the answers!

Write the similar-sounding words that should have been used in the sentences above into the chart below.

Sentence number	Similar sounding word(s) that should have been used
11. 1	
12. 2	
13. 3	
14. 4	
15. 5	
16. 6	
17. 7	
18. 8	
19. 9	
20. 10	

Test 28: Tricky spellings

Unscramble these words, which are often misspelt. The meanings are there to help you work them out. The first one has been done for you.

Scrambled word	Clue	Answer
scab nee	the lack of something	absence
21. call ooh	intoxicating drink	
22. panacea per	what something looks like is its...	
23. height	the one after seventh	
24. luau befit	opposite of ugly?	
25. sub en sis	you might set one of these up to make money	
26. rec met ye	a burial ground	
27. comet item	a group of people who talk and make decisions	
28. rid fens	people we like to spend time with	
29. vice deer	something signed for from the postman is...	
30. a boat lorry	a place where experiments might take place	
31. lie nelsons	what you might feel when you are on your own	
32. aria germ	a ceremony uniting two people	
33. acnes ryes	needed	
34. binge hour	a person who lives next door to you	
35. sure up	to chase after something or someone	
36. cross sis	a tool used to cut things with	
37. cent seen	a group of words that make sense as a unit	
38. ed roils	a member of an army	
39. wired	strange	
40. an villi	a bad guy	

/**40**

Test 1	Test 2	Test 3	Test 4	Test 5
/10 %	/10 %	/40 %	/35 %	/50 %
Date _____	Date _____	Date _____	Date _____	Date _____

Test 6	Test 7	Test 8	Test 9	Test 10
/10 %	/10 %	/35 %	/30 %	/40 %
Date _____	Date _____	Date _____	Date _____	Date _____

Test 11	Test 12	Test 13	Test 14	Test 15
/10 %	/10 %	/35 %	/40 %	/40 %
Date _____	Date _____	Date _____	Date _____	Date _____

Test 16	Test 17	Test 18	Test 19	Test 20
/10 %	/10 %	/40 %	/50 %	/10 %
Date _____	Date _____	Date _____	Date _____	Date _____

Test 21	Test 22	Test 23	Test 24	Test 25
/10 %	/25 %	/50 %	/10 %	/10 %
Date _____	Date _____	Date _____	Date _____	Date _____

Test 26	Test 27	Test 28
/30 %	/35 %	/40 %
Date _____	Date _____	Date _____

Colour each box in the correct colour to show how many questions you got right.
0%–20% = yellow, 21%–50% = green, 51%–70% = blue, 71%–100% = red
This will help you to monitor your progress.